What a mess
and The little elephant

M

Macmillan Education

What a mess

Penny upset her milk.
Look at this milk,
Mum said to Penny.
What a mess.

Penny upset her
painting water.
Look at this water,
Mum said to Penny.
What a mess.

Penny fell over in the park.
Her boots were wet and
her coat was muddy.

Look at you,
Mum said to Penny.
What a mess.

Come on Penny, said Mum.
We must go home.
Come on Digger, said Penny.
We must go home.

Penny and Mum went
into the house but
Digger wanted to dig
in the garden.

Then Dad came home.
Look at Digger, he said.
What a mess.

Dad, Mum and Penny went
into the garden.
Digger jumped up at them.
Look at us, said Penny.
What a mess.

The little elephant

Let's go to the zoo,
Dad said.
Yes, said Tom and Jenny.
Let's go to the zoo.

Mum put on her sun hat.
Dad got a bag of nuts.
Tom and Jenny got in the car.
Off we go, said Dad.

Can we see the elephants,
said Tom.
I want to ride on an elephant,
said Jenny.

Look at that big elephant,
said Tom.
Jenny gave the big elephant
a nut from Dad's bag.

Look at that little elephant,
said Jenny.
Look out Mum, said Tom.

The little elephant has got
Mum's hat, said Tom.
Mum was cross.
Make him give it back,
she said.

Give him the bag of nuts,
said Jenny.
The little elephant was greedy.
He took the nuts and
he dropped the hat.
And then . . . . he stood on it.